£4.50

Printed and Published in Great Britain
by D. C. THOMSON & CO., LTD.,
185 Fleet Street, London EC4A 2HS.
© D. C. THOMSON & CO., 1994

ISBN 0 85116 574-5

Growing Paynes

OOH! LOOK AT ALL THOSE LOVELY TOYS.

CAN I HAVE THAT BALL, MUM?

Suddenly —

OW!

?!

OUCH!

BUMP!

WATCH, WHAT... MARY! I HAVEN'T SEEN YOU FOR YEARS.

WHO'S MARY?

I'M SORRY I BUMPED YOU.

DON'T WORRY! IS THIS THE NEW BABY? ISN'T SHE LOVELY, PERCY?

HUH! MUM ALWAYS GOES GAGA OVER BABIES!

POOH! WHAT A NASTY SMELL.

SO WHAT? YOU USED TO SMELL LIKE THAT, TOO.

WAAGH! I DIDN'T!

QUIET, PERCY. YOU'LL WAKEN THE BABY.

Too late!

WAAGH!

THERE, THERE, MY LITTLE COOCHY-COO!

YOU SOUND JUST LIKE THAT, TOO.

I DO NOT! I'M NOT A BABY LIKE THAT.

Soon after —

OH, DEAR! I'M SORRY PERCY DISTURBED BABY.

IT'S ALL RIGHT. I'LL JUST GO AND CHANGE HER.

LOOK, MUM. I'M SKIPPING.

SHERMAN TORTOISE

In the grounds of Blithering Hall lives Sherman, a very special sort of tortoise. He is protected by Colonel Crickett's platoon of garden crawlies.

This is Scythe the gardener — Sherman's enemy.

GROWL!

SNIP!

TELL YOU WHAT I'D REALLY LIKE TO CLIP.

SNICK!

THAT MARIGOLD-MUNCHING REPTILE, THAT'S WHAT.

DOES HE MEAN US, SHER?

SILLY OLD GEEZER.

AND IT SO HAPPENS I HAVE A FIENDISH IDEA TO DO JUST THAT.

I LOVE BEING NASTY — NASTY — NASTY — NASTY.

BAM!

BANG!

THUD!

CRUMP!

DANGER SCYTHE AT WORK!

SHERMAN, HOW ABOUT WE GO RAID SCYTHE'S VEGETABLE PATCH?

YIKES! WHASSAT?

DROTTLE! RATTLE!

OHMEGOSH!

YUK! YUK!

FSSSCH!

IT'S A DRAGON.

I HOPE IT DOESN'T BREATHE FLAME AND SUCHLIKE.

THAT ONLY HAPPENS IN FAIRY TALES.

As the clock strikes three.

PHEW!

CUPPA TIME.

I'M SENDING A SQUAD TO MAKE SOME TEENSY CHANGES TO MR SCYTHE'S MACHINE.

VROOM!

Under the dragon —

INSIDE, LADS, AND REMEMBER THE TOOLS.

MISSION ACCOMPLISHED, COLONEL.

SCREECH!

OH, I DO LIKE IT WHEN A PLAN STARTS TO COME TOGETHER.

C

The blue buffoon changes back to Eric.

CUDDLES and DIMPLES

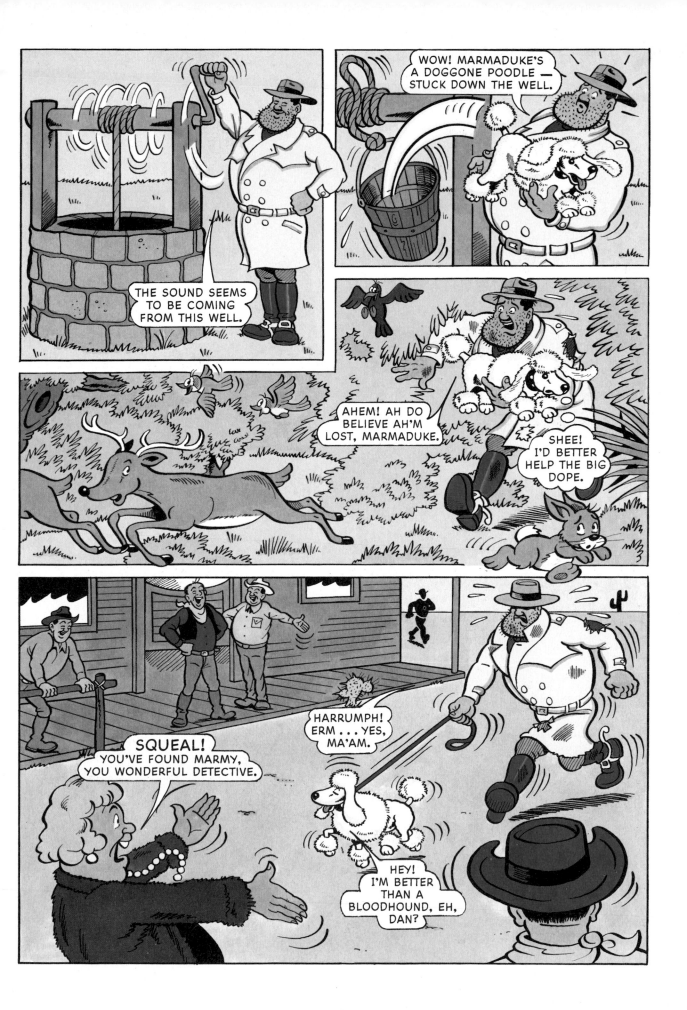

BARNEY *the Wonder Winger*

BULLY BEEF and CHIPS

THAT FILM HAS GIVEN ME A FEW IDEAS TO TRY OUT ON CHIPS.

PLAZA CINEMA

ANIMAL TRAPPER

NOW SHOWING

TUM-TI-TUM.

TRAP NUMBER ONE IS READY.

WHOOSH!

HOO!

EEEK!

YOU FELL FOR THAT ONE, CHIPS.

YOU RAT, BEEFY.

Later —

CHUCKLE!

THE DANDY BOOK

WAIT FOR TRAP NUMBER TWO, FOLKS.

HO! HO! THE DANDY BOOK IS GREAT.

THE DANDY BOOK

YAROO!

YANK!

GOTTIM!

THE DANDY BOOK

LET ME DOWN, BEEFY.

WHY DON'T YOU HANG AROUND FOR A MINUTE, OLD BOY.

Soon —

THIS MUST BE CHIPS TRYING TO TRICK ME — SOME CHANCE.

BUT I'LL HELP MYSELF TO HIS BANANAS.

CHOMP! CHOMP!

RUN FOR IT, BEEFY. WILD GORILLA ON THE LOOSE.

PULL THE OTHER ONE, YOU LUMP.

Winker WATSON
Break period at Greytowers School and Winker Watson, World Champion Wangler, and his pals are enjoying a spot of rugger . . .
GREYTOWERS SCHOOL SPORTS CENTRE
WA-HEY! NICE TRY, WINKER!

... but not for long if Mr Creep has anything to do about it.

THIS IS OUTRAGEOUS! YOU ARE FILTHY! A DISGRACE TO THE SCHOOL!

I WILL INSPECT YOU ALL AT 09.00 HOURS TOMORROW — SCRUBBED AND SPOTLESS.

GROAN! IT'S LIKE THE ARMY.

SOAP

FIRST, DOWN WITH THE ESCAPE HATCH.

JONES MINOR, CAN I BORROW YOUR SOLDIER MODELS?

JONES MINOR TOY BOX

YOU WILL SCRUB THOSE UNIFORMS THEN YOU WILL SCRUB YOUR GRUBBY SELVES.

HAH-HAH! I'LL LOCK THEM IN UNTIL IT'S DONE.

3RD FORM DORM

WATCH OUT, GUYS. I'VE GOT A WANGLE BREWING.

GOOD OLD WINKER!

YOU MIGHT AS WELL TAKE THE WHOLE PLATOON.

HTY-HO, INKER.

GOOD LAD.

February

THANK YOU, GRAHAM. I'M ON MY WAY!

And, almost sixty years after he first found the mummy . . .

. . . the professor is ready to do it all over again.

While, at the scene of the crime . . .

← STAIRS

CHECK THE STAIRS. THE ROBBERS MIGHT STILL BE IN THE BUILDING.

LIGHTS MUST HAVE GONE . . . I'D . . . HEY! WHO'S THAT HIDING UP THERE?

DON'T MOVE! I'M ARMED!

I SAID DON'T . . . OH, NO! NO!!

STAY BACK! AAAARGH!!

BLAM BLAM

WHAT WAS THAT?

IT SOUNDS LIKE SOMEONE'S IN TROUBLE!

HE'S FAINTED. GET HIS TORCH!

SARAH . . . STAY BACK! I THINK I KNOW WHY HE FAINTED.

IT'S KHARIS!

HE'S ALIVE!

Meanwhile, unaware of the events inside, the professor races to the museum.

YOU CAN'T GO IN THERE, SIR!

I'VE GOT SECURITY CLEARANCE! LET ME THROUGH, PLEASE!

WHY WOULD ANYONE WANT TO STEAL AN ANCIENT MUMMY?

ESPECIALLY WITH SO MANY OTHER, MORE VALUABLE EXHIBITS . . . EH??

LOOK! IN THE SKY!

WHAT THE . . .?

But for now a missing mummy will have to wait . . .

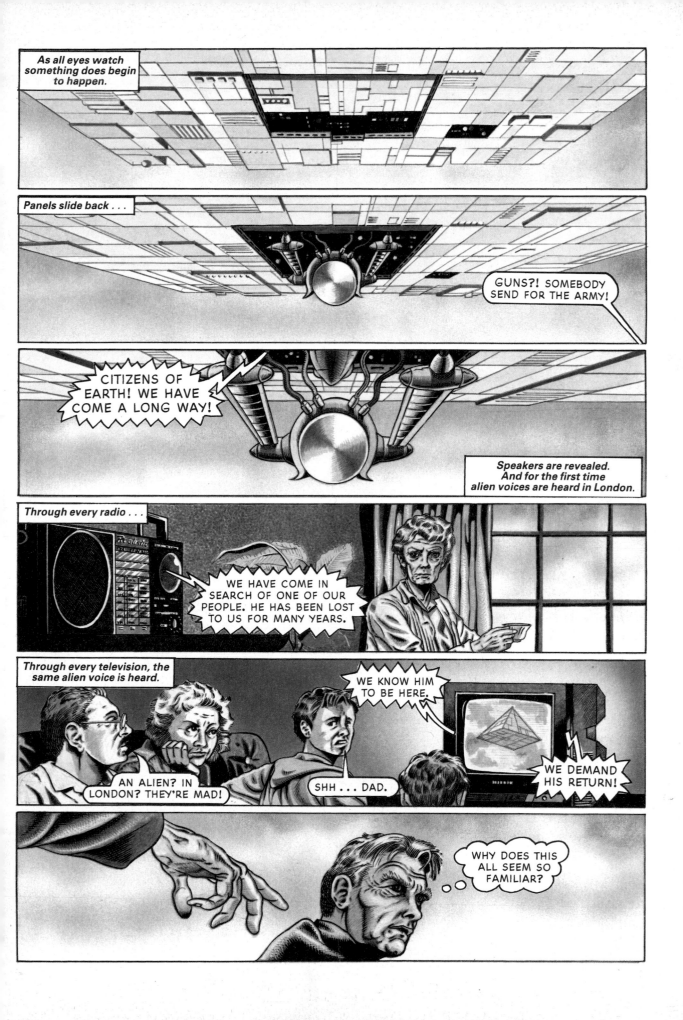

I'M AFRAID YOUR GRANDCHILDREN ARE MISSING!

NOT ANY MORE! LOOK!

DON'T SHOOT. PLEASE!

HE'S BEEN HURT!

TELL YOUR MEN TO HOLD THEIR FIRE!

YOU HEARD HIM, MEN!

And, as the professor and his discovery are reunited . . .

GRANDFATHER, WE FOUND THE MUMMY.

. . . An alien light engulfs them . . .

And for the first time human beings stand within an alien space craft!

GREETINGS, EARTH PEOPLE. I AM HORUS.

I KNOW!

AND I ALSO RECOGNISE ISIS, OSIRIS AND ANUBIS . . . THE EGYPTIAN GODS!

NOT GODS. MERELY VOYAGERS.

WE VISITED YOUR WORLD THOUSANDS OF YEARS AGO.

YES. IN EGYPT, WHERE ONE OF YOUR CREW MEMBERS WAS INJURED AND WRONGLY ENTOMBED!

... THERE IS ONE THING ...

And ...

WHERE ARE THEY GOING?

THEY'RE LEAVING!

WE'LL COME BACK ... SOON.

And for two young minds and one not so young, all eager to learn ...

... A whole new universe is opened up for them!

KEYHOLE KATE

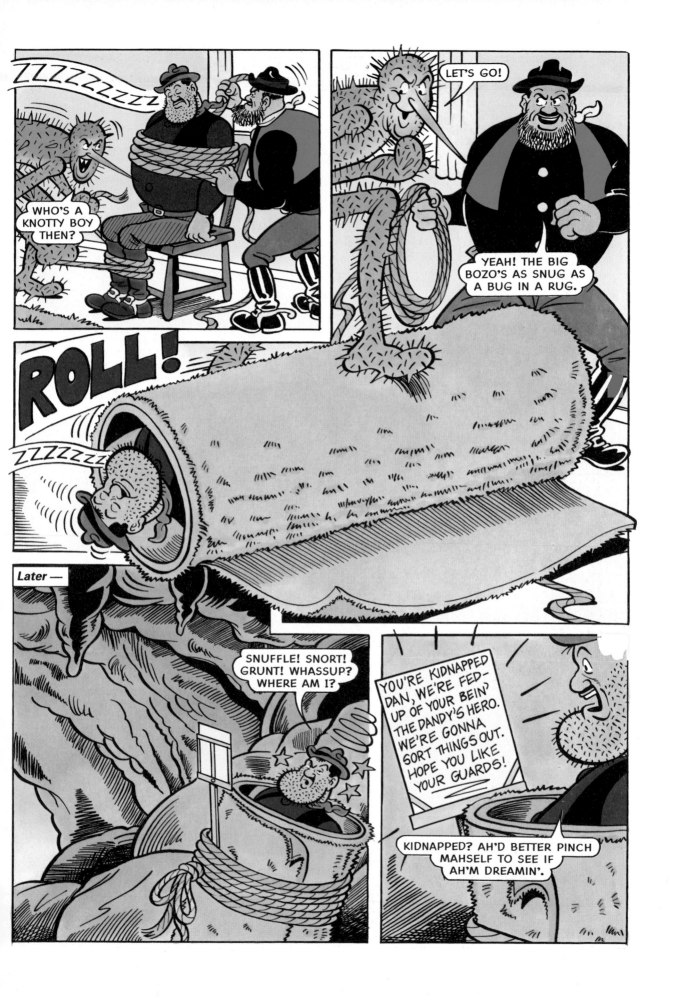

Cuddles and Dimples

Bananaman

ERIC IS IN HIS GARDEN TALKING DRIVEL

THE NICE WEATHER'S GOT MY FLOWERS REALLY SPRINGING UP.

THANK YOU, MY SUN!

SEEING AS IT'S SUCH A LOVELY DAY I'LL SHOW YOU ROUND THE REST OF THE GARDEN.

SCREAM!

T-TIDAL WAVES WEREN'T FORECAST TODAY. THIS CALLS FOR AN EMERGENCY 'NANA.

ROAR!

Seconds later —

A BUNCH OF YOUR BEST BANANA ICE LOLLIES, PLEASE.

DOWN THE HATCH WITH THE ENTIRE BATCH!

A BLAST OF ICY 'NANA BREATH WILL STOP THIS WAVE IN ITS TRACKS.

BLAST!

HEH! THIS CALLS FOR A COLD SNAP.

SNAP!

THERE! BACK IN THE SEA WHERE YOU BELONG.

TOSS!

SPERLOOSH!

Meanwhile, orbiting the Earth is a strange craft —

With an equally strange crew of Dr Gloom and General Blight —

GRR! IT'S THAT INTERFERING FOOL, BANANAMAN.

HAVE NO FEAR, GENERAL. THIS WEATHER SHIP OF OURS WILL LEAD TO HIS DOOM.

SNARL! IT HAD BETTER. YOU'RE MAKING HEAVY WEATHER OF IT SO FAR.

ONCE BANANAMAN IS TAKEN CARE OF I SHALL RULE THE WORLD, AS WELL AS THE DANDY!

FINISH HIM OFF THIS TIME, GLOOM — OR ELSE!

R-RIGHT AWAY, YOUR GENERALNESS.

SUPER SEA SUCTION NOZZLE ON, GENERAL.

OH, GOODY!

Down below —

THANKS TO ME, THE PLANET IS SAFE FROM TIDAL WAVEY THINGS.

I'D BETTER CHECK THE LATEST WEATHER FORECAST.

FOR YOU, LITTLE ERIC, THE WEATHER WILL CONTINUE VERY STORMY. HEE-HEE!

GOSH! IT'S MY ARCH ENEMY, GENERAL BLIGHT.

THAT IS THE END OF THIS STORM WARNING.

AND THE END OF YOU, SONNY!

MUNCH! THIS IS A JOB FOR SOMEONE BIGGER THAN ME.

KERBOOM!

YES! ME, FOLKS! THE MIGHTY BANANAMAN!

MOLLY

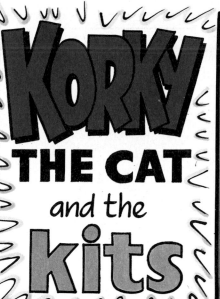

KORKY THE CAT
and the kits

DINAH MO

Twas the night before the night before Christmas.

I HAVEN'T MADE UP MY MIND WHAT I WANT FOR CHRISTMAS.

THIS LOOKS PROMISING.

O WALK O RUN O DON'T TOUCH!

NOT BAD AT ALL. HO-HO!

MY TOYS!

CLOSED DUE TO SHORTAGE OF TOYS!

OUT! AND DON'T COME BACK!

CHORT!

The night before Christmas—

NOW TO VISIT THE OTHER TOY SHOPS BEFORE I WRITE MY LETTER TO SANTA.